JUMP

BY CHARLY EVON SIMPSON

DRAMATISTS
PLAY SERVICE
INC.

NOTE ON BILLING
Anyone receiving permission to produce JUMP is required to give credit to the Author as sole and exclusive Author of the Play on the title page of all programs distributed in connection with performances of the Play and in all instances in which the title of the Play appears, including printed or digital materials for advertising, publicizing or otherwise exploiting the Play and/or a production thereof. Please see your production license for font size and typeface requirements.

Be advised that there may be additional credits required in all programs and promotional material. Such language will be listed under the "Additional Billing" section of production licenses. It is the licensee's responsibility to ensure any and all required billing is included in the requisite places, per the terms of the license.

SPECIAL NOTE ON SONGS/RECORDINGS
Dramatists Play Service neither holds the rights to nor grants permission to use any songs or recordings mentioned in the Play. Permission for performances of copyrighted songs, arrangements or recordings mentioned in this Play is not included in our license agreement. The permission of the copyright owner(s) must be obtained for any such use. For any songs and/or recordings mentioned in the Play, other songs, arrangements, or recordings may be substituted provided permission from the copyright owner(s) of such songs, arrangements or recordings is obtained; or songs, arrangements or recordings in the public domain may be substituted.

JUMP was first produced as a National New Play Network Rolling World Premiere by PlayMakers Repertory Company (Chapel Hill), Confrontation Theatre and Milagro (Portland), Actor's Express (Atlanta), and Shrewd Productions (Austin) with support from the David Goldman Fund for New American Plays. For more information, please visit nnpn.org.

JUMP was developed, in part, at SPACE on Ryder Farm, the Kennedy Center in association with NNPN, and as part of Chautauqua Theater Company's New Play Workshop series, 2018, underwritten by the Roe Green Foundation.

author's note.

The first draft of *Jump* was mostly written in the fall of 2016 during a five-day-long writer's retreat that I went on just weeks after my dad's father passed away. By the time I was working on the second draft of the play, in the winter of 2017, my mom's father had passed away. A few days after the first public reading of this play, another family member passed away. I moved through that year thinking about death and acknowledging the deaths around me, but I wasn't sure if I ever felt grief. I didn't really dwell on the losses. And I never really connected the dots that *Jump* probably deals with family and grief because my family and I were dealing with grief ourselves.

While writing the play, my focus was on memory and connection. My plays are often haunted, necessarily, by memory. The memory of what was, the memory of what wasn't, and the pain and pleasure associated with both seem to be at the heart of so many of the plays I write. I was curious about how we remember, what we remember, and how what we remember shapes us. Memory provides us with a map, a way of understanding, a way of uncovering. But memory is also faulty, imprecise, and influenced by emotion and hindsight. As a human being in the world with a memory and memories, I have been struck by the times memories have stayed clear and the times memories have escaped me. I have also been struck by how sharing something I remember can connect me to a stranger while pushing me further away from a loved one.

My instinct is to say that for *Jump*, I dug through the character Fay's memory and found this story and a number of other memories sitting there, like it was in a diary sitting on her desk. That feels as much the truth as the real truth sounds—which is I saw a flash of Fay on a bridge and asked myself how she got there. I was living in and creating the world of her memory, digging my way through layers of grief and mental health and connection. And where I ended up is here...in a funny, sad, hopefully somewhat-magical play that asks us to think about who we connect to and why, where connection can be found and why, and how do we ultimately care for each other.

characters.

FAY, black woman, younger sister, 28, hooked on her vape now that she doesn't smoke cigarettes

JUDY, black woman, older sister, 31, still smells the lingering cigarette smoke

HOPKINS, any race, a fellow bridge walker, late 20s, a bit of a smart-ass

DAD, black man, Fay and Judy's dad, 58, not doing well

place.

a city with a bridge that goes over a gorge
a bridge that people like to linger on
a bridge that makes people nervous
but also
a house near the bridge
with at least a living room
and a bedroom where one can see the bridge out of the window

we go between these spaces easily
things roll on and off
or maybe they are just created on top of each other
it is a melding of space
but we do know when we are in one space versus another
until we just don't

time.

this is a world of past, present, and some fantasy mixed in.
it is late summer to early fall.

note.

the flickers are like a dimming before the lights go out during a storm. there may need to be some sound with it, a distorted splash, a slight buzz, something that makes us feel Fay's confuddlement for a moment.

there's no need to tell the audience the timeline. they'll be fine.

slashes indicate when the next person should start speaking.

there is no intermission for a reason.

JUMP

1.

Six weeks ago.
The bridge.
The lights on the bridge are the only lights on.
That and the lights from cars passing by.

Fay enters.
On the bridge.
She stands and looks out on the water.
A runner runs across, behind her, doesn't take her in.
Then a cyclist.

Fay pulls something out of her pocket.
She wishes it were a pack of cigarettes, but instead
Fay vapes.
She wants to toss the ash, the butt, into the water,
flick it off her fingers.

She vapes.
She vapes.

She decides to throw it anyway, the vaporizer.
She throws it off.
She watches it fall.

From above, another one falls.
Fay catches it without looking.

She vapes.
She vapes.
She wishes she had a cigarette.
Because she wants to flick the cigarette off her fingers and
into the water.

She decides to throw the vape anyway.
She throws. She watches it fall.

From above, another vape falls.
Again and again.
It happens several times.
On loop.
Until the lights bump off.
The sound of traffic horns takes us into the next scene.

2.

Present day. Around 1 P.M.

Fay. Vapeless.
She is in front of a house.
It is daytime.
There are birds chirping but Fay is not the type of person who cares to listen to some birds chirping.

She is waiting, but she doesn't really look like she is waiting.
She doesn't pace or look at her watch.
She stands in place.
She looks forward or to the side.
She chooses a direction.
She focuses on it.
We imagine she is watching someone walk across the street.
Maybe she is doing a math problem in her head.
It is that kind of concentration.

She brings her hand to the back of her head, as if she has a headache, and closes her eyes.

Judy walks up in the opposite direction.
We hear her footsteps before we see her.
She wears blue heels.
Kitten heels. Cute but practical.
Fay is in Converse.

Fay doesn't have to open her eyes to see Judy.
She knows she's there.

JUDY. Sorry I'm—

FAY. It's okay.

JUDY. Traffic. The bridge.

FAY. Yeah.

JUDY. What's wrong with your head?

FAY. Headache.

JUDY. Want some Tylenol?

FAY. Took some. Didn't work.

> *They stare at each other.*
> *Fay looks Judy up and down.*

JUDY. I hate it when you do that. / It's creepy.

FAY. What's on your nails?

JUDY. What?

FAY. Your nails…?

JUDY. …polish…

FAY. They look like Fabergé eggs.

JUDY. How do you know what a Fabergé egg looks like?

FAY. Why wouldn't I?

> *Brief moment.*

He likes that? On you?

JUDY. Who?

FAY. Your husband.

JUDY. He's not my—

FAY. Common law at this point.
Does he like it?

JUDY. What?

FAY. The polish.

JUDY. I never asked.

FAY. Why not?

9

JUDY. It's not for him.

FAY. Don't say it is for you.
It is a lie when we say it is for ourselves.

JUDY. Who are you right now?

FAY. I just think we should be / honest.

JUDY. I thought you were a fem/inist…

FAY. It has nothing to do with / my feminism.

JUDY. So you don't like any kind of makeup?

FAY. I didn't / say that.

JUDY. Now my eyeshadow is some sign of patriarchal / hullabaloo.

FAY. I mean at its core…

JUDY. For you maybe it's about someone else.
Maybe that is what it is for you.

FAY. It's not.

JUDY. But you just said—

FAY. I say a lot of things.

JUDY. You say a lot of things to piss me off.

> *The lights flicker.*
> *Judy doesn't notice.*
> *Fay does.*

FAY. Did you see—

JUDY. You smell like cigarettes.

FAY. No I don't.
I vape now.

JUDY. Still around smokers.
Still gross.

FAY. You're gross.

> *A small moment.*

JUDY. When is he supposed to get here?

FAY. 1.

JUDY. It's almost 1:30.

FAY. I'm aware.

JUDY. He's late.

FAY. You were late.

JUDY. I—

FAY. He's always late.
You're always late.
It's a family trait.

People always expect me to be late.
But I'm not.
I'm early.

JUDY. Do you want a prize?

FAY. No.
No.
I'd just like some recognition, you know?
I'd like for us to acknowledge my contribution to timeliness.

> *The lights flicker.*

Hey do you see how the light is…

> *She looks up at Judy.*
> *Judy looks off into the distance.*

Are you listening to me?

JUDY. I just have things to do.

FAY. So do I.

JUDY. Okay.

FAY. I do.

JUDY. Okay.

FAY. You always think I don't, but I do.

JUDY. I didn't say anything Fay.

FAY. Fine.

JUDY. Fine.

FAY. Fine.

> *The lights flicker.*
> *They keep flickering.*
> *It is weird that the sun flickers like a lamp would.*
> *It is weird that Judy doesn't notice.*

Are you seeing the light?

> *There is the sound of heels.*
> *Just like the beginning.*
> *Fay turns to look for the sound of the heels, which is in the*
> *opposite direction of where Judy is standing.*
> *Fay turns and sees nothing.*
> *The lights stop flickering.*
> *Fay turns back to Judy.*
> *It is like the scene restarts.*
> *Judy smiles.*

JUDY. I'm sorry I'm late.

FAY. What?

JUDY. I'm late.

I'm sorry.

Don't be an ass about it.

The traffic on the bridge was nuts.

> *Fay stands there staring at Judy.*
> *She rubs her head.*
> *She looks around.*

What?

FAY. …

JUDY. …

FAY. Déjà vu.

I guess.

JUDY. Doesn't exist.

FAY. …Well, maybe then I think I don't feel well.

JUDY. Don't do that. Don't try to get out of this.

FAY. Out of what?

JUDY. Whatever this day is.

> *Beat.*
> *There is the ding and buzz of a text.*
> *Fay looks at her phone.*

FAY. I mean, come on.

JUDY. What?

FAY. He's going to be even later.

JUDY. Did you expect anything else?
From Dad, I mean.

FAY. No.
I guess not.

JUDY. We could go in, I guess.

FAY. What?

JUDY. We could go in and—

FAY. And what?

JUDY. Decide which of Mom's things we want to fight over.

FAY. I don't want anything.

JUDY. Neither do I.

FAY. Maybe he just wants our help cleaning.

JUDY. Well, I can't do that now.
I just can't.

FAY. Cleaning?

JUDY. Whatever this is.

FAY. Judy…

JUDY. What? Don't give me that face…

      A moment.

FAY. Maybe he is just telling us about it.

JUDY. Or maybe he has other news.

FAY. He found someone else.

JUDY. He is in the witness protection program and nothing he has ever told us has been true.

FAY. He is gay and is finally telling us.

JUDY. He isn't our real dad.

FAY. He has another, secret, family.

JUDY. He is broke.

FAY. He is dying.

JUDY. He is selling the house.

      Fay and Judy look at each other.

13

The game has ended.

The lights flicker.
Fay only slightly acknowledges it.

FAY. Only the far-off ones, Jude.
We weren't supposed to say what he is actually going to say.

JUDY. We don't know he is actually going to say that.

FAY. I mean, he's been staying with Auntie. He doesn't live here anymore. Hasn't since, what, three weeks after Mom died?

JUDY. Maybe he'll want to rent it…

FAY. Doubt it.

A small moment.

You should've moved in.

JUDY. God no.

FAY. You and Russell coulda been living rent-free.

JUDY. I had no desire to live in our childhood home.

FAY. One of our childhood homes. The most homelike.

JUDY. For you. Maybe.
This place caused me to be the new girl in high school. This caused years of untreatable trauma.

FAY. Maybe your personality just caused it.

JUDY. Ha.
You could have moved in…

FAY. Too far from my job.

JUDY. Not that far.

FAY. I guess I always sort of knew he wouldn't move back. Why should he?

JUDY. I guess none of us wanted to be here after she was gone…

A small moment.

FAY. I always liked how you could see the bridge from here.

JUDY. Mom always liked it.

They look at the bridge.
But we can't see it.
The lights flicker.

14

FAY. You aren't noticing anything weird about the light?

JUDY. No…

JUDY. They stopped someone
from jumping yesterday

FAY. Oh Yeah?

> *A moment.*
> *The lights flicker.*

FAY. Let's just go in.
I think I need to go inside.
I think I need water.
Or something.

JUDY. Fine…

> *Fay goes and unlocks the front door.*
> *She turns to look at Judy.*

FAY. You coming?

> *Judy looks around and then goes toward the door.*

JUDY. Yeah.

> *Judy smiles and goes inside the house.*

DAD. Hey Fay.

> *The lights flicker.*
> *Fay turns around.*

> *Dad enters.*
> *He is rushing toward the house.*
> *He looks worn out.*
> *Fay gives a halfhearted smile when he comes up.*

Sorry I'm late.
Sorry.

FAY. It's fine.

DAD. No it's not.
I know it's not.
Your mother would say it wasn't.

FAY. If Mom were still here, you'd be on time.

DAD. True.

> *They look at each other stone-faced.*
> *Dad gives her a small hug.*

It is uncomfortable.

You doing okay?

FAY. Yeah.

DAD. Yeah.
Me too.

FAY. Good.

DAD. Yeah.
Good.

> *Fay and Dad linger outside.*

FAY. Where'd you park the car?

DAD. Around the corner.
Fucking parking.

FAY. I know.
It's gotten worse.

DAD. I know.
Only a year later and it is so much worse.

FAY. I know.

> *Fay turns to go in.*
> *Dad hesitates.*

Ready to go in there?

DAD. Oh. Uh…

FAY. Or we can wait out here for a bit. / That's fine too.

DAD. I didn't want to tell you over the phone.

FAY. What?

DAD. Uh, well, I'm selling the house.

FAY. Yeah.
I guessed…

DAD. Oh.
Oh.
Really?

FAY. Yeah.

DAD. Yeah?

FAY. Yeah.

DAD. Hmm.

FAY. I mean, what are you going to do with this big house? Of course, you could rent it out but / you'd hate being the landlord.

DAD. I'd hate being a landlord.

FAY. It wouldn't be your strength.

DAD. Yeah.
And it's not like you could be the landlord. I mean, maybe Judy could—

FAY. I mean, I think I could.

DAD. Oh really?

FAY. I don't want to be the landlord, but I think I could do it.

> *Dad nods.*

DAD. Mmmhmmm.
Well.
I'm selling the house. I found an apartment. And…

FAY. Auntie kick you out?

DAD. No. No. Just…it's time.

FAY. Right. Yeah. Right.

DAD. So we need to…there are boxes…

FAY. Okay.

DAD. All right.

I don't know how long it will take…there's only so much left…it shouldn't be that much…but you and Judy's room…

FAY. We can get it done. We're a team.

> *Dad gives Fay a small look.*

DAD. Good. Good. Okay then. Let's uh…

> *Dad begins to walk into the house.*
> *Fay follows slowly.*
> *They shut the door behind them.*

3.

Four weeks ago. Evening.

Fay walks across the bridge.
Her vape is in her hand, but she does not use it.
She is not sure she wants to vape.
When she is about a quarter of the way across the stage, she stops.

On the opposite end of the bridge is Hopkins.
He stands looking out.
He smokes a real cigarette.

Fay looks at him. Stares at him.

Hopkins looks up. He sees her, but doesn't say anything and looks at the water.
Fay turns towards the water.
They both are bridge walkers, staring out at the water for a moment.

Then Hopkins pulls out his phone and, very low, begins to play a song like "Another One Bites the Dust" by Queen. * We in the audience perhaps can't make it out right away, but Fay hears it and turns to him.*

Hopkins is in his own world. He listening to the song and mumbling the lyrics to himself.

We see Fay be annoyed with the song and the music and the noise and Hopkins but as the song goes on she begins to move with it. She begins to mumble the song too.

And when Hopkins turns and sees that she is mumbling along too, he turns it up. And he sings louder.

And Fay then sings louder.
Louder and louder.
(Not that they really know all the words.)
When they are screaming the song, Fay turns.

* See Note on Songs/Recordings at the back of this volume.

They begin an un-choreographed dance of sorts, in their own worlds but not.
They move, they pretend to play guitar, they fall to their knees, they jump up and down.
They do anything they need to do.

Fay and Hopkins do the entire song.
They do the whole thing.
They commit.
When it is done, they stand out of breath.
They breathe.
We hear their breath.
The lights from cars hit their faces.
The sounds of cars, the background music to their laughter.
When they stop, Fay walks over to Hopkins.

FAY. I'm Fay.

HOPKINS. I'm Hopkins.

> *They stand awkwardly.*
> *For a while.*
> *A nice long while.*
> *Whatever magic was there before has faded to normalcy.*
> *They are just on a bridge now.*
> *It is just evening now.*
> *They are just two strangers now.*

FAY. Nice to, uh…

HOPKINS. Yeah.

FAY. I needed that.
I think.

> *Fay walks a little bit away from Hopkins.*
> *She pulls out her vape.*

HOPKINS. Oh

FAY. Huh?

HOPKINS. Nothing

FAY. Okay

She begins vaping.

HOPKINS. You're one of those.

FAY. Excuse me?

HOPKINS. A *vaper.*
You vape.

FAY. And?

HOPKINS. Too good for an old cigarette?

FAY. What are you, a purist?

HOPKINS. I just like my tobacco to kill me, you know?

> *He chuckles.*
> *Fay doesn't.*

FAY. We had a nice moment. Why ruin it with small talk?

> *Fay begins to walk further away.*
> *Hopkins runs to catch up with her but stops as soon as she*
> *turns around.*

HOPKINS. I'm sorry. I'm an ass.

FAY. It is not endearing.

HOPKINS. I didn't say it—

FAY. Too many men think they can admit to being dicks and suddenly it is okay.

HOPKINS. Ass.

FAY. What?

HOPKINS. I said ass. Not dick. Dick seems gender-normative.

FAY. There are women who are dicks, who have dicks.

HOPKINS. But isn't it just easier since everyone has an ass to say ass?

FAY. What about the one person who doesn't have an ass?

HOPKINS. I feel sorry for her.
Him.
Them.
That person.
…
…

...
I don't know what to say to you now.

FAY. You could say nothing.

> *Hopkins nods.*
> *He looks out.*
> *She looks out.*
> *They say nothing.*
> *For a few moments.*

Are you a serial killer?

HOPKINS. Um no.

FAY. My sister...she has my location. We, like, share our locations with each other.

HOPKINS. What?

FAY. She can see where I am. All the time. She can. On her phone. It's a thing.

HOPKINS. Not if you lose your phone.

> *They stare at each other.*

I realize that's a little sketchy to say.

FAY. Yeah.

HOPKINS. I'm not a serial killer.
I am just a guy. On a bridge.
A guy who likes to walk on a bridge.

FAY. Okay.

HOPKINS. If I am sketching you out, I can leave.

FAY. No.
No.
Sorry.
It's okay.

> *They quietly stand for a minute.*
> *Then Fay breathes audibly and turns to go.*

HOPKINS. Have a nice night.

FAY. Huh?

HOPKINS. Night. Nice. Have one.

FAY. Oh…thanks.

HOPKINS. See you around?

FAY. Here?

HOPKINS. Yeah.

> *Fay shrugs.*
> *Fay turns and walks a ways away, and then turns and watches.*
> *Hopkins looks out over the side of the bridge.*
> *He grips the metal handrail.*
> *He holds on to it.*
> *He squeezes it.*
> *This barely registers on his face.*
> *And then suddenly he lets go and steps back.*
> *He slowly exits. Fay follows him with her eyes.*

4.

> *Present day. Around 6 P.M.*

> *Fay and Judy look like they've been packing for a while.*
> *A little sweat and dust sits on their foreheads.*
> *They are in their childhood room.*
> *There are two twin beds.*
> *If there are walls, they are covered in posters with boy bands*
> *and, perhaps, one Miles Davis poster from when one of the two*
> *was going through their slightly more sophisticated phase.*

JUDY. We should share locations. Like on our phones.

FAY. What?

JUDY. We can follow each other. / It's a thing.

FAY. I know. You asked me before.

JUDY. I did?

FAY. Yeah. I said I didn't want you stalking me.

JUDY. I wouldn't be stalking you.

FAY. Why else would you want it?

JUDY. I don't know. Safety. If you ever go missing.

FAY. You could go missing too you know.

JUDY. If *either* of us goes missing we can… listen it is a thing.

FAY. It is a thing helicopter parents do.

JUDY. Smart. Parents. Or in this case sisters…

FAY. Don't mom me, Judy.

JUDY. Mom didn't even know how to work a smartphone.

They sit in quiet.

We should've taught her.

FAY. Well, it's not like she would have gotten a lot of use out of it.

Judy looks at Fay, hurt.

What?! Learning how to use a smartphone would not have stopped her cancer.

JUDY. I just don't like it when you…when you say things in… that way.

FAY. Well, we all have our ways of handling things. You have yours and I have mine.

JUDY. Hmmph.

A long moment.

This room never changes.

FAY. How would it…unless we changed it?

JUDY. I understand the logistics, Fay.

FAY. It's dusty.

JUDY. How could it not be unless we changed—

FAY. I got it.

JUDY. When's the last time you were here?

FAY. Well I've been here, but not up…here.

JUDY. Yeah.

I think it was right after she died.

FAY. Probably for me too.

JUDY. Right before he moved out.

FAY. Probably.

JUDY. Yeah.

FAY. Yeah.

> *Judy stands in front of what was her bed.*

JUDY. You remember how we'd flop into bed?

FAY. You don't still flop?

JUDY. I guess I don't.
Come on, let's flop.

FAY. What?

JUDY. Let's flop.

FAY. Judy…

JUDY. Come. On.

> *Judy stomps her foot.*
> *Fay rolls her eyes and stands.*
> *Judy and Fay each stand backwards in front of a bed, facing us.*
> *They look at each other.*
> *They nod.*
> *They jump and fall backwards onto the beds.*
> *They laugh.*
> *They turn to each other.*

> *Judy gets up.*
> *She stands backwards in front of the bed, facing us.*
> *She looks where Fay stood before.*
> *She nods.*
> *She jumps and falls backward onto the bed.*
> *She laughs.*
> *She turns to look at Fay.*

> *Judy gets up and repeats the process.*

> *Fay stops smiling.*
> *She watches, worried.*

> *When Judy gets up to do it a fifth time, Fay stands between Judy and her bed.*
> *Judy looks like she is going to jump and fall back anyway.*
> *Fay pushes Judy.*

The lights flicker.

FAY. JUDY!

> *Judy turns and puts her hands on her hips.*

JUDY. Get out of my way pipsqueak.

FAY. You've been doing it over and over again.

JUDY. What are you talking about?

FAY. Judy, you've done this—

JUDY. Stop trying to ruin my fun.
You are always doing shit like this.

FAY. …

JUDY. What?

FAY. I just…

JUDY. Can you move?

> *Fay moves out the way.*
> *Judy falls back onto the bed.*
> *Fay watches.*
> *Judy laughs and does it again.*
> *Fay watches.*
> *Judy goes to do it again. She looks at Fay expectantly.*
> *Fay gets up and does it with her, just like the first time.*
> *At the end of the fall back, Fay turns to look at Judy.*
> *Judy smiles.*
> *This time she stays on the bed, resting on it and sighing.*
> *Fay exhales.*

I can't believe they made us share a room.
Really it was Mom. I know it was Mom.
She always wanted us closer.
I always wanted to be like, *Mom, we are three years apart. Let us live.*
Maybe that's why she forced us into this room together.
Probably why.

> *Judy looks at Fay, who is staring at Judy.*

Why are you looking at me like I'm crazy?

FAY. …

JUDY. What is it, Fay?

25

FAY. Nothing.

JUDY. What did I hurt your feelings or something?

FAY. No.

JUDY. I didn't think you cared about being close to me.

FAY. Well that's not true.

JUDY. Whatever.

> *Judy gets up and looks out the window we can't see.*

I did like this view though.

> *Fay absentmindedly nods.*

You can see straight through to the bridge here. It's so clear tonight.

FAY. Yeah.

> *Judy turns and looks at Fay*

JUDY. Maybe we should get to it then?

> *Fay at first doesn't move, but eventually goes over to the boxes.*
> *Fay begins to put the boxes together*

We can do the three box thing.

FAY. What three box thing?

JUDY. Donate. Keep. Trash.

FAY. Oh.

Yeah.

Sure.

What do you think Dad's doing downstairs?

JUDY. Staring at the boxes.

FAY. Staring out the window.

JUDY. He doesn't look good.

FAY. Yeah, I know.

JUDY. You should spend more time with him.

FAY. He's so far.

JUDY. Fay...

FAY. What? He is...

JUDY. I try to go every Sunday.

FAY. I know. You rub it in. Every. Sunday.

JUDY. It's just a lot. It would be nice to have you there too. Sometimes. At least.

FAY. All right, all right.

> *She lines the boxes up in a row.*
> *Fay reaches behind one of the beds.*
> *There is a basket there.*
> *She brings it center stage.*
> *In the basket are some things you'd expect to find in a teenager's bedroom.*
> *Judy rests on the bed.*
> *Fay begins to take something out and sees Judy relaxing.*

Um, I'm not doing this alone.

JUDY. Most of this is your stuff. I moved a lot of mine out before.

FAY. There is a lot of your stuff here too, sister.

JUDY. I had to pack all of Mom's stuff.

FAY. A year ago…and not all / of her stuff.

JUDY. Almost all of it.

FAY. Come on, Judy!

JUDY. I call seniority. Older sister privileges. I'm allergic to dust consideration.

FAY. God. You're so annoying sometimes.

JUDY. You love me.
I'll help from here.

> *Judy smiles.*
> *Fay stares back at her.*
> *Judy excitedly points to a poster in the basket.*
> *Fay begrudgingly pulls the poster up.*
> *It is a Backstreet Boys poster.*

You need to trash that.

> *Fay throws it in the trash box.*
> *She holds up a violin.*

My violin!!

FAY. Donate?

JUDY. Yeah. I guess.

> *Fay throws it into the donate box.*
> *She holds up a teddy bear.*

FAY. Mr. Willakers!

JUDY. Trash?

FAY. No! Keep it for the future kids.

JUDY. What if there are no future kids?

FAY. Keep it anyway. You loved it. Mom had to, like, tear it away from you when you went to sleepaway camp.

JUDY. Well…you loved that blonde guy in the Backstreet Boys, but we've decided to get rid of that so…

FAY. Noted. Whatever. Fine. Trash.

> *Fay throws it into the trash box.*
> *She holds up the book* The Lion, the Witch and the Wardrobe.

The Lion, the Witch—

JUDY. Duh. Keep.

> *Fay throws it into the keep box.*
> *She holds up rollerblades.*

Donate.

> *Fay puts them into the donate box.*
> *She holds up a hot-pink sweater.*

FAY. I loved this thing.

JUDY. You did.
But we should trash it.
Burn it.

FAY. Aww come on.

JUDY. You ever going to wear it?

FAY. God no.

JUDY. Trash.

FAY. …Fine…

> *She throws it in the keep box.*
> *She holds up a photo.*

JUDY. What's that?

FAY. A picture of you, me, and Mom in the park.

JUDY. Let me see it.

> *Fay comes and sits down next to Judy on the bed.*
> *They sit close to one another. The closest they've been so far.*

FAY. Did Dad take this?

JUDY. Mmmmm... I don't think so. I don't think he was there that day.

FAY. What day?

JUDY. Don't you remember?

FAY. Obviously not.

JUDY. It was the first time Mom walked us across the bridge.

FAY. No! Really? We got a photo of that?

JUDY. Yeah.
Mom wanted us to feel like tourists.
In fact, I think she lied and said we were tourists.

FAY. I don't remember that.

JUDY. You were young.

FAY. Not that young.

JUDY. Young enough.

> *Fay gets up and drops the photo into the keep box.*
> *Judy stretches.*

Are you hungry? I'm hungry.

FAY. It's dinner time.

JUDY. And I want dinner.

FAY. We should do more...

JUDY. Later.

> *Judy flops onto the bed again.*
> *The lights flicker.*

FAY. Judy?

JUDY. Yeah?

FAY. Are you okay?

JUDY. Yeah, weirdo. You okay?

FAY. Yeah. Yeah. I am.

JUDY. Okay.

FAY. Okay.

>*A moment.*

Maybe we should share locations or whatever.

JUDY. I don't want a pity share.

FAY. I don't even know / what that means…

JUDY. Should we order something to eat?

FAY. Are you gonna share your location with me?

JUDY. It was my idea. So.
Hungry?

FAY. Yeah.

JUDY. Chinese?

FAY. Sure. Dad'll eat that.

JUDY. Do you have the number? I don't have the number…

FAY. You don't remember the number?

JUDY. You do?

>*Fay pulls out her phone and begins dialing.*
>*Judy falls back on the bed.*
>*She stifles her laughter.*
>*Fay watches her as she orders.*

FAY. Hi, I'd like to place an order… One General Tso's Chicken and one Sesame Chicken…

>*Judy then stands on the bed.*
>*She looks over the edge of it.*
>*Her smile is gone.*

Uh-huh. Yes, it's 6316 Post Road.

>*Judy looks up. Fay is still looking at her.*
>*Judy smiles.*

Great.

>*Judy sits down on the bed. Fay sits next to her.*
>*And we transition to the next scene.*

5

Three weeks ago. Evening.
Fay stands center.
On the bridge.
Cars going by.
She looks at her phone as she leans on the railing.

Hopkins enters.
He is listening to music.
(FYI, Hopkins is not the sort to have those big Bose head-phones.)
When he sees Fay, he slows. He smiles lightly and then walks up to her.

Whenever Fay says something that can be interpreted as flirtatious, she says it non-flirtatiously.
She isn't trying to flirt. She isn't flirting.
Even if Hopkins thinks she is.

HOPKINS. You should be careful.

> *Fay jumps back slightly.*

Sorry.

FAY. You scared me.

HOPKINS. Yeah. Sorry.
I just...you should be careful. With your phone.

> *Fay glares at him.*

Don't want to drop it.
Off the edge.

FAY. Right.
Right.

> *They stand awkwardly.*

This is getting to be a thing.

HOPKINS. Not my fault you're here all the time.

FAY. Not my fault you've started interrupting my bridge time.

HOPKINS. Hey, this was my bridge time before you. You only started showing up last week.

FAY. I've been coming my whole life.

HOPKINS. Every week?

FAY. No.

HOPKINS. Well.

FAY. Sometimes in your life you have to walk the bridge. Sometimes you don't.

HOPKINS. I get that.

> *A long moment.*

So, you are in a time in your life that you have to walk the bridge?

> *Hopkins cozies up next to Fay.*
> *Fay takes a few steps away.*

FAY. I guess.

HOPKINS. I'm just making small talk.

FAY. I thought we decided we weren't good at that.

HOPKINS. We decided that?

FAY. We should have.

> *They look to each other and then look out at the water.*
> *It is quiet for a while.*
> *Fay, despite herself, relents.*

Are you from here?

HOPKINS. I thought we weren't—

FAY. Listen, answer or don't. You aren't doing / me any favors.

HOPKINS. No. Not originally.

FAY. So this bridge is, like, new to you.

HOPKINS. That's a weird way of / thinking about it.

FAY. No. No… This is my bridge. Like I grew up with it. I came here as a kid. It's my bridge. Maybe you have another bridge somewhere that is your bridge. Maybe this is your substitute bridge.

HOPKINS. Not many bridges where I'm from.
This is as close to a bridge that is mine that I'm going to get.

FAY. Hmm.

A long moment.

HOPKINS. Tell me about your first time.

FAY. What first time? Like...my first time, first time, because I'm not / sure you should be privy...

HOPKINS. Oh.

No.

Sorry.

I mean...

The first time you came to *your* bridge.

FAY. Oh.

Ha.

Um.

My mom brought me.

She brought us.

She walked us across when I was nine and Judy, my sister, was twelve.

Maybe she wanted to tell us something?

But she didn't talk really. Not while we walked.

And it's a long walk.

She'd always just look over the water and then smile to us as we frowned back at her.

HOPKINS. Oh man...

Your mom didn't...

like...

She didn't like...jump...did she?

Fay stares at Hopkins for a moment before she answers him.

FAY. No.

God no.

No. No. No.

HOPKINS. Oh. Oh. Good! Good to know she is alive and well.

FAY. Oh. Well. She isn't.

HOPKINS. Oh.

Sorry.

FAY. Cancer.

A year ago.

HOPKINS. Oh good.

I mean, not good.

I mean—

FAY. You really thought that I'd end this particular story with my mom jumped off the bridge?

HOPKINS. I wasn't sure.

It could make sense, you know?

Lonely girl walks the bridge because her dead mother killed herself here.

That's someone's story.

Somewhere anyway.

FAY. Who said I was lonely?

HOPKINS. I assumed.

FAY. I can walk alone and not be lonely.

HOPKINS. Sure.

But.

FAY. I could be an introvert.

HOPKINS. Are you?

FAY. Yes.

HOPKINS. Introverts can be lonely.

FAY. You're probably fucking lonely.

HOPKINS. Yeah.

You'd be right.

That's why I assumed.

> *Fay glances at Hopkins.*
> *They stand on the bridge.*
> *It's chilly. They shiver. Slightly.*
> *A car honks on the bridge.*
> *They both turn to look at it because it is something to look at.*
> *They then return looking out.*

FAY. Why do you?

HOPKINS. What?

FAY. Why do you walk the bridge? Is this a time in / your life…

HOPKINS. Oh I…

FAY. Don't tell me…your dad died on a bridge or something.

A moment.

HOPKINS. Uh, well…

Fay's smile turns to a frown.

FAY. Oh shit…

HOPKINS. I told you…that is someone's story even if it isn't yours.

FAY. Shit. I'm sorry.
I'm sorry.

Hopkins turns to her and smiles.

HOPKINS. I'm shitting you.

FAY. What?

HOPKINS. I'm shitting you, Fay.

FAY. You are?

HOPKINS. Yeah.

FAY. Fuck you, asshole.

HOPKINS. Sorry.

FAY. Asshole.

They turn and look out.
Silence for a bit.

So why the fuck do you walk then?

HOPKINS. *(Without a pause.)* I was going to jump.

Fay rolls her eyes.

FAY. I'm not falling for it.

HOPKINS. Nothing to fall for.

FAY. Stop.

HOPKINS. I'm not doing anything.
Not now.

FAY. You're serious?

HOPKINS. As a heart attack.
Or as jumping off a bridge.
Which, I guess, is also pretty serious.

Fay isn't sure of what to say.

> *Or do.*
> *She fidgets for a few moments.*

Sorry.
You asked / me.

FAY. What stopped you?

> *Hopkins shrugs.*
> *Fay tries another tactic.*

So what's keeping you from jumping off bridges these days?

Sorry.

Sorry.

Sor—

HOPKINS. Would it be awkward if I said you?

FAY. Me what?

HOPKINS. That you are the reason I didn't.
I'd be lying… Partially anyway…

> *Fay and Hopkins stare at each other.*

I don't know why.

FAY. You seem okay…

HOPKINS. I often do.

FAY. So what's wrong?
Like…why…did…you want to jump in the first place?

HOPKINS. Things suck.

FAY. Sometimes.

HOPKINS. All the time.

FAY. But that's life.

HOPKINS. Yeah and some people aren't equipped to handle life so…we jump.

> *Fay lets the words hit her.*

FAY. Have you read about the survivors?
The ones who've jumped and lived?

HOPKINS. I try to avoid it.

FAY. I read a little. About them.

They all say they regretted it.

Like as they were falling that they regretted it.

HOPKINS. Maybe that's why they survived.

Their hearts and souls weren't in it.

Really in it.

If you want to die, maybe you've got to have that push.

That need.

FAY. You're romanticizing or glorifying it…or…or…

HOPKINS. I'm spitballing—

FAY. You really think that no one who has succeeded has felt regret?

HOPKINS. No.

I'm not saying that.

I'm just saying it is hard to leap. To jump.

FAY. I'd say it seems like the opposite.

HOPKINS. We are built to try to carry on. Survival is in our genes. There are, have been, so many atrocities in the world that could have left entire groups of people dead if it weren't for that pesky gene, instinct, whatever, that tells us to keep going.

FAY. How Darwin of you.

HOPKINS. I'm serious.

FAY. You are basically saying that those who are successful are somehow stronger or more focused, more committed than those who weren't. That's what you're saying.

HOPKINS. I…

Um.

You think I'm being ridiculous?

FAY. I think some people jump and regret it and some don't and it has no bearing on how you land.

I also think it is pretty shit to tell someone who failed at suicide that their heart wasn't in it.

HOPKINS. Did you fail at—

FAY. No.

No.

Fuck no.

I just mean in general. In fucking general it would be shit to tell someone, to tell you, that.

HOPKINS. I feel like that could go both ways.

Fay shrugs.

You're probably right.

They look out.

FAY. One man landed at the perfect angle. Like his legs were fucked up, but he managed to, like, protect his spine and organs or whatever.

HOPKINS. Yeah.

FAY. I just think it's luck

HOPKINS. Some would say it's God

FAY. I'm not one to say things like that.

HOPKINS. Neither am I.

Fay really looks at Hopkins.

FAY. Death doesn't work the way you say it works.

HOPKINS. I'm not saying—You know I'm not saying your mom wanted to die or—

FAY. Dude, I'm an adult who knows how cancer works. I'm not going to be rocked by some new-age bullshit just because some man said it to me on a bridge on a starry fucking night okay?

HOPKINS. Okay.

FAY. You're the one telling fairy tales.

HOPKINS. …

FAY. …

HOPKINS. …

FAY. …

HOPKINS. …

FAY. I'm sorry you wanted to jump.

Hopkins shrugs.

I'm sorry you want to jump.

Hopkins shrugs.

Maybe it is a good thing your heart isn't in it…

HOPKINS. I thought you said that's a shit thing to say.

FAY. Yeah but I said it.

> *There is a quiet.*
> *We notice where they are again.*
> *They notice where they are again.*

HOPKINS. You want to get outta here?

FAY. And go where?

HOPKINS. I don't know.
To not here.

FAY. Um…

HOPKINS. Forget it.

FAY. Wait a damn second.
Can you ask me again…another time?
Can we go another time?

HOPKINS. You can say no.

FAY. I know.
I'm asking for a raincheck.

HOPKINS. Fay, you don't have to—

FAY. I want a raincheck. We just talked about fucking suicide…
I'm not really in the mood to… I came to the bridge because I want
to be at the bridge, okay?

I understand if you need to go…not be here…

HOPKINS. I'm fine.
A raincheck.

FAY. A raincheck.

> *Fay looks out over the bridge.*
> *Hopkins looks too.*
> *He grips the metal handrail.*
> *After a few moments, Fay gently places her hand on top of his.*

6.

Present day. Around 7 P.M.

Back in the house.
Downstairs.
In the living room.
There is a big, leather, La-Z-Boy kind of chair there.
But Fay sits cross-legged on the floor in front of two Chinese
food takeout containers.
She eats from one with a fork.
Dad enters from the kitchen.
He has a cup in his hand.
It looks like water but is probably vodka.

DAD. Sure you don't want anything to drink?

FAY. I've got some water in my bag.

DAD. Suit yourself.

> *He sips his drink.*

So.

FAY. Yeah?

DAD. How's it going up there?

FAY. Fine. Found some funny stuff.

A Backstreet Boys poster.

Judy's violin.

Just deciding what to donate, what to throw away…you know.

DAD. Yeah. Good.

FAY. Do you remember how we used to flop on the bed, Judy and
me? We'd make so much noise and you and Mom would—

DAD. Yeah. I remember.

> *They sit in silence for a moment.*

Work okay?

FAY. Yeah. Yours?

DAD. Yeah.

A moment.

And you've been...uh...you've been okay?

> *Fay half smiles.*

FAY. You asked this earlier.

> *Dad just looks at her.*

I'm fine. I'm okay.

DAD. What does okay mean?

FAY. God, Dad, it was your word so / I don't know.

DAD. So you are not okay?

FAY. I didn't say that.

DAD. So you are okay.

FAY. Yeah, sure, I'm okay.
Okay as I'm here and I'm breathing and what more / can you ask for?

DAD. Now I don't know if that's the answer you should be giving me.

FAY. I'm not sure you really want to know.

DAD. Why wouldn't I?

> *Judy enters.*
> *She holds a piece of chicken in her fingers.*

JUDY. This isn't as good as I remember.

> *Fay looks up at her.*
> *Dad takes a bite of chicken.*

DAD. The food quality really has gone down.

FAY. I think they are under new ownership. I think I read that. Saw that. Or whatever.

DAD and JUDY. Huh.

> *They both take bites of their respective chicken pieces.*
> *Fay looks at them both.*
> *They turn and look at her.*
> *They smile.*
> *She smiles.*
> *Fay takes a bite of the chicken.*

FAY. I'm not sure we've gotten this since...

41

JUDY. Yeah. Is that weird? Like wouldn't most people eat more Chinese food after their mother dies. We ate less.

FAY. We had an unhealthy relationship with pizza.

DAD. I'm glad we didn't order pizza.

FAY. Are you still eating pizza for every meal?

DAD. I get a vegetable in there from time to time.

JUDY. From time / to time...

DAD. Listen, it is like being a bachelor again and when I was a bachelor...

FAY. You ate pizza and beer.

DAD. Right and now I—

FAY. Eat pizza and vodka and beer and bourbon...

> *Dad sips his vodka.*
> *He stares ahead.*

JUDY. Fay...

DAD. And what do you do? Are you a perfect glimpse of healthy behaviors?

FAY. Is anyone?

DAD. Then perhaps stick to what you know.

FAY. Dad—

DAD. What do you know anyway?

FAY. I know you've been a mess since Mom died and that—

DAD. That's enough, Fay.   JUDY. Fay!

FAY. Dad, I'm just—

DAD. I'm going to work on the kitchen.

> *Dad gets up with his drink.*
> *He exits.*

JUDY. Well...you done did it now.

> *The lights flicker.*

FAY. Shit.

JUDY. He'll drink himself into a stupor.

FAY. And that's my fault? How about you take some of the blame?

Or Mom? I'd love to not be alone with his...his...

> *The lights flicker.*

JUDY. I'm going back up. I'm not hungry anymore.

FAY. Great. You too.

JUDY. You two never could talk anything out.

FAY. What?

JUDY. Always running to opposite ends of the house. When you fought. Never quite knowing what to say to each other...ever.

FAY. I don't like confrontation. I don't like awkwardness...

JUDY. Mom isn't here to play middleman anymore. And I won't. I can't.

FAY. Why not?

> *Judy gets up and exits.*
> *The sound of shoes.*
> *Fay looks up and around.*
> *Judy walks back in.*
> *Judy picks up a piece of chicken with her fingers.*

JUDY. One for the road.

> *She then exits again.*
> *The lights flicker.*
> *Dad enters.*
> *He picks up a piece of chicken with his fingers*

DAD. One for the road.

> *He then exits again.*
> *Fay sighs.*

7

Two weeks ago. Evening.

Fay. On the bridge.
She is alone.
Cars go by her.
She just looks forward.
She is alone like this for a bit.
Then Hopkins enters.

HOPKINS. This is getting—
FAY. I wait for you now.
HOPKINS. You do?
FAY. I come.
Every day.
Now.

Not just because of you.
HOPKINS. Okay.
FAY. To be fair the weather has been especially nice these last few days.
HOPKINS. Okay.

> *Very small moment.*

I usually come on Thursdays.
FAY. …Oh.

> *Small moment.*

How are you, Hopkins?
HOPKINS. Uh. Well. I'm all right.
FAY. All right?
HOPKINS. All right.
FAY. Really?
HOPKINS. Sure.
FAY. Come on.
HOPKINS. How are you?

FAY. No. Don't change the subject.

HOPKINS. I'm not.
I'm being polite.
I'm asking how you are.

FAY. I'm fine. But how are you, really?

HOPKINS. Fine.
How are you really?

> *Fay grumbles.*

FAY. Jesus.

HOPKINS. What?

FAY. I'm really fine…but you…

HOPKINS. But what?

> *Moment.*

Fine is the worst answer, by the way.
No one is fine.
Someone can be all right, but no one is fine.

FAY. Oh?

HOPKINS. Yeah. Like fine is our Pavlovian response to that question.
It is like using the word interesting in an essay.
You shouldn't do it.

FAY. You write many essays these days?

HOPKINS. As a matter of fact, I do.

FAY. Really?

HOPKINS. Yeah. I'm in grad school.

FAY. *You're* in grad school?

HOPKINS. Yeah. What of it?

FAY. Nothing…

> *They stand on the bridge.*

I'm an assistant. I assist. In an office.

> *They stand on the bridge.*

You're really all right?

HOPKINS. Sure. I mean… I've been worse, you know?

Fay nods.

You?

FAY. I've been better.

Hopkins nods.

HOPKINS. Nice night for a bridge walk then.

FAY. Yeah…

Yeah.

They then look forward for a long time.

8.

Present day. Around 9 P.M.

Back in Judy and Fay's old room.
Moonlight comes through the window.
Judy and Fay sit amongst boxes and old things.
Fay sneezes.

JUDY. Bless you.

FAY. Thank you.

Every time I sneeze I taste Chinese food.

JUDY. Gross.

FAY. Yeah.

Fay throws something in a box.

I think I'm over this.

JUDY. It's not like we were mentally prepared.

FAY. I mean, in a way, we were.

In that we knew it was bound to happen.

JUDY. Yeah but…

I didn't wear the right shoes.

Fay and Judy look down at her shoes.

Sometimes I swear I can hear Mom walking down the hallway.

FAY. You hear them too?

JUDY. Hear what?

FAY. The shoes?

JUDY. Oh…uh…no?

I just mean that sometimes I'm sitting and I swear my spidey-senses sense Mom. Like I can hear her in her slippers as she comes down the hallway in my apartment, but she was never in my apartment so I don't know why I have that memory.

Maybe you have the same thing.

FAY. I heard them earlier. When you came. Earlier.
I feel like things have been repeating.

> *Beat.*

JUDY. You sound like a crazy person.

FAY. Judy!

JUDY. I'm just saying.
It's not far off. Not considering how many drugs you took—

FAY. I don't know why you think of me as this crazy druggy…

JUDY. You just hung out with that / terrible crowd

FAY. You actually have no idea who I hung out with because you were so in your / own world.

JUDY. I was a senior. You were a freshman. I didn't have time to / think or care about you.

FAY. Exactly so how can you say anything about that crowd?

JUDY. There'd be so much smoke.
And this room.
Come on.
I'd find it

FAY. I did…sometimes.
Sometimes.
But you did it too.
You probably did more than me.

JUDY. Not possible.

FAY. Perfectly possible, Ms. Perfect.

In fact, I know Mom caught you once because she told me.

Judy looks angry.

JUDY. She told you what?

FAY. How she found you passed out.
Scared her half to death.
She didn't tell Dad though.
So just—

JUDY. Okay.
Sorry.
Sorry.

It was a bad night.
That night was a bad night.
I never did shit like that again.

FAY. Maybe you should have.

> *The lights flicker.*
> *A short silence.*

I'm serious about things being weird.
Like I actually think something may be wrong with me.
Mentally.
Okay?
I wasn't trying to—

JUDY. Maybe you should check it out…maybe it is, like, vertigo.

FAY. I'm not…like…dizzy, Judy.

JUDY. I don't know, Fay. I'm not a doctor.

> *Dad appears in the doorway.*
> *He doesn't walk in the room.*

DAD. All right up here?

FAY and JUDY. Yeah.

DAD. Good.

FAY. You okay down there?

DAD. Yeah.
Mostly done.

JUDY. That's good.

DAD. Want to call it a night soon?

48

FAY. Yeah. Sure.

>*Dad looks at the room.*

DAD. When you girls were little...we'd stand outside this door at night and hear you whispering to each other.

FAY. I don't remember that.   JUDY. There's no way we did that.

DAD. You guys had your own language. I'd want to come in. Tell you girls to go to sleep, but your mom would push me down the hall. Told me to mind my business.

FAY and JUDY. As you should.

DAD. Yeah. Well...I'll be downstairs.

FAY. Be down soon...

DAD. Sounds good.

>*Dad exits.*
>*The lights flicker.*
>*Fay rubs the back of her head.*

JUDY. It could be a brain tumor.

FAY. What?

JUDY. You feeling...weird...it could be a brain tumor.

>*Fay angrily looks at Judy.*

What?
It's possible.
And there'd be precedent.

FAY. Shut up, Judy, for Christ's sake.

JUDY. You should get it checked.
Mom didn't get it checked and—

FAY. I get it.

JUDY. It would just be sad to leave—

FAY. JUDY!

JUDY. Sorry.
Sorry.

FAY. Fine.

JUDY. We should just take care of ourselves.
You know?

FAY. Yeah, I guess.

JUDY. No. Really. Take care of yourself.

FAY. Okay.

> *The sisters are quiet.*
> *They each do their own version of twiddling their thumbs.*

JUDY. I don't do my nails for him.

FAY. What?

JUDY. Earlier…you said…
I don't do my nails for him, but I wear heels.
He likes me in heels.

FAY. Do those even count as heels?

JUDY. He likes a little lift, okay?
So I lift.

FAY. Okay.

JUDY. I usually put flats in my bag.

FAY. Oh?

JUDY. Just in case I want the heels off.

FAY. Judy, do you even like the heels?

> *Judy laughs.*

JUDY. Ah. Well.
I like them about as much as I liked pointe during ballet.

FAY. So not at all?

JUDY. I like the idea. I like how it looks in photos. I like how my legs look in them.
I like that he likes it.

FAY. But you don't…just… Take them off, Judy.

JUDY. I don't have flats.

FAY. Here.

> *Fay takes off her Converse.*
> *She passes them over to Judy.*
> *Judy stares at them.*

JUDY. What?

FAY. My feet are bigger than yours. They'll fit.

JUDY. You can't take my shoes.

FAY. I'm not taking your shoes.

JUDY. What will you wear?

> *Fay goes back to the basket and pulls out another pair of Converse. They are dirtier and well worn.*

FAY. Old habits die hard.

JUDY. This is so—

FAY. My shoes are probably sweaty and have a fungus growing in them, but hey, to each his own…
You want 'em now or not?

> *Judy takes off her heels.*
> *Fay grabs them.*
> *Judy puts on the Converse.*

JUDY. I think this is the nicest thing you've ever done for me.

FAY. Shut it.

JUDY. Seriously.

> *Fay throws the kitten heels in the donate box.*

Hey!

FAY. Fuck those shoes, Jude. Fuck 'em.

> *Judy looks down at the Converse on her feet.*

JUDY. They don't match the outfit.

FAY. You can make it work.

> *Fay goes to exit.*

You going to come down?

JUDY. Right behind you.

> *Fay goes to exit, but turns and stands in the doorway.*
> *Judy goes to the window.*
> *She looks out of it.*
> *She is there for a while and then she turns to the bed.*
> *She gets on it and she jumps.*
> *She jumps on the bed.*
> *Higher and higher.*
> *She jumps and jumps and jumps and jumps.*

51

9.

One week ago. Evening.

Loud honking noise brings us back to the bridge.
Fay is there alone.
It is much like the first scene of the play.
Fay.
And her vape.
And she is there on the bridge.
And there is a world going on around her, but she is not a
part of it, but she is also not not a part of it.
She pulls out her phone and looks at the time.
She then takes a drag(?) of her vape.
She looks at the time.

Hopkins enters.
On a bike.
This is new.

FAY. Biked?

HOPKINS. Yeah.
Healthier to bike.

FAY. Oh.

HOPKINS. I'm trying to be healthier.

FAY. I guess that's good.

HOPKINS. My lungs don't agree.
This is why I usually don't try to be healthier.
This is why staying in bed for hours on end is actually preferable to
most other activities.

FAY. You don't say.

HOPKINS. I do say.
I say it.

Anyway, I'll have some stupid amount of miles and hills to go up
and down later so fuck me, you know?

FAY. Yeah.

You…want to be healthier now.

HOPKINS. No. No. Not really.

It has just been…suggested to me…as a way of…facilitating…life…?

FAY. Endorphins and shit.

HOPKINS. Yeah.

FAY. Really healthy people kill themselves too.

They stare at each other.

HOPKINS. That's probably not what you should—

FAY. I mean, we just like to believe it is lonely ass people and it's not always lonely ass people.

HOPKINS. Yeah.

I get it.

FAY. Yeah.

The wind gusts.
Hopkins pulls out his cigarettes and starts to smoke.

HOPKINS. This is becoming less enjoyable. Running into you. You either lecture or demand silence.

FAY. I…I can't dispute that. So why do you keep coming?

HOPKINS. Uh, well, the view.

FAY. Oh.

HOPKINS. It's true.

FAY. Yeah. Me too.

A small moment.

But also. Now.

I feel… I feel it's my responsibility.

To be here. Now.

HOPKINS. What?

FAY. To make sure you don't…do…it.

Fay motions with her hands what looks like something jumping off a platform.

HOPKINS. Oh god, Fay. You said you weren't coming here for me.

FAY. You sort of gifted me a strange amount of power.
Or something.

HOPKINS. I'm not sure I did—

FAY. I just feel like I am now *your* guardian angel and it is my responsibility to keep you as safe and alive as possible.

HOPKINS. You don't have to be here to save me, Fay.

FAY. You aren't just coming here every Thursday planning on jumping and then not?

HOPKINS. No.

FAY. I mean, not that I thought you were...

HOPKINS. I'd just come at another time, Fay.
If I really...
Don't start coming at other times.
Not because I am going to
Not because I will jump
But because
You could be here all the time
That's not smart. You should have a life.
I won't come if you don't come.
That sounds dirtier than I want it to
I just mean that
I won't
I'll be here. For a while.
I'm not

FAY. Got it.

HOPKINS. Okay.

FAY. Okay.

HOPKINS. The urge is not...
It's not with me right now.
Not today.

FAY. Okay.

HOPKINS. And you don't know very much about me.

FAY. True.

HOPKINS. And you clearly come here to work your own shit out too so...

FAY. …yes…

> *A moment.*

What are you in grad school for?

HOPKINS. …why…?

FAY. You said I don't know much about you. I'm trying to learn more.

HOPKINS. Anthropology.

FAY. So you are trying to be Darwin?

HOPKINS. It was a huge mix-up. I thought Indiana Jones was an anthropologist, but he's not. He's an archeologist…which is just like a more specific kind of anthropologist, but…no Temple of Doom.

FAY. That could be a good thing.

HOPKINS. I guess. What about you?

FAY. What?

HOPKINS. I share. You share. That's how a conversation works.

FAY. Oh…well…

I think I may have a brain tumor.

HOPKINS. What?

FAY. Things just keep being…weird.
Like not…real?
I dunno.

HOPKINS. So no one has looked at your brain and thought oh there is a tumor in there?

FAY. No.

HOPKINS. So you are just late-night diagnosing yourself over the computer?

FAY. Kind of.

HOPKINS. Maybe you got it all wrong.
Maybe I'm *your* guardian angel and I am here to tell you to stop.
You don't have a brain tumor.

FAY. There was this book by this young doctor who totally got cancer—

HOPKINS. Then go to the doctor.

FAY. And my mom had cancer.

HOPKINS. Then go to the doctor.

FAY. My sister just has me thinking about it and—

HOPKINS. Then go to the doctor, Fay.

FAY. Are you going? To a doctor.
Like a psychologist or something.

> *Hopkins shrugs.*

HOPKINS. No.

FAY. Shouldn't you—

HOPKINS. Yeah, yeah, sure, right, okay.

> *Fay starts to laugh.*

What?
What are you laughing about?

FAY. We're both sick in the head.

> *Fay laughs harder.*
> *It is a bad pun.*
> *But it makes her laugh.*
> *And Hopkins begrudgingly begins to laugh too.*
> *And they are laughing.*
> *On the bridge.*
> *Until there is the sound of shoes and the lights flicker.*
>
> *Fay immediately stops laughing.*

10.

> *Present day. Around 10 P.M.*
>
> *Fay and Dad downstairs in the house.*
> *There are some boxes in front of them.*
> *It's late.*
> *The Chinese food containers sit off to the side on the floor, empty.*
> *Dad looks a little harried.*
> *Fay looks tired.*

DAD. So everything is…?

FAY. Yeah.
Made a donate box.
Multiple boxes.
Donate. Trash. Keep.
Like all the things say to do.

DAD. What things?

FAY. I don't know.
Articles.
Books.

Anyway. Goodwill is going to pick it up tomorrow. The donate boxes.

DAD. Good. Good.

FAY. Are you sure you don't want to go through it?

DAD. No.
Why would I?

FAY. Keepsakes.

DAD. Yeah. Well. It's all up here.

> *He points to his head.*

FAY. Okay.

DAD. And there are photos.

FAY. Oh, I put a bunch of photos in a box. I figured you'd want to take them to your new place.

DAD. You take 'em.

FAY. Dad.

DAD. I don't want 'em.

FAY. Come on, Dad…

DAD. I'm serious. I don't want 'em.
You.
You take 'em home.

> *A short moment.*

FAY. Fine…fine.

> *A long moment.*

DAD. Do you want some whiskey?

FAY. You've got whiskey too?

Dad gives her a look.

It is just a question.

DAD. I got whiskey. You want?

FAY. ...Sure...

> *Dad exits to the kitchen.*
> *Fay fidgets in the space alone.*
> *Dad reenters with a bottle of whisky in one hand and two small glasses in the other.*

DAD. Kept them here especially.
In case we needed to...partake.

> *They both smile.*

Here.

> *He hands a glass to Fay.*
> *She holds it as he opens the whiskey and pours some into her glass.*

You still smoke?

FAY. No.
I vape.

DAD. Is that healthier?

FAY. Yes.
No.
I don't know.
Hope so.

DAD. You should get healthy.

FAY. Okay. So should you.

DAD. Your mother would have wanted that.

FAY. Sure.
But you, you don't want me to get—

DAD. I wouldn't be saying it if I didn't want it also.

> *He holds his glass out for a toast.*

FAY. To?

> *Dad shrugs.*

Old homes?

They look each other in the eye.
They clink glasses.
They take a sip.
They feel it going down.

DAD. It's good.

FAY. Yeah.

I guess.

I don't usually have it so…

DAD. It's good.

They sit in silence.
The smell of the whiskey filling their nostrils.
Fay plays with her glass a bit.
She moves the whiskey around.
She swirls it.

Just leave it be, Fay.

Fay puts the cup down forcefully.

What? What I'd do—

FAY. I don't want to fight.

DAD. I'm not fighting.

FAY. Okay.

She picks the glass back up.
She smiles and motions to him for approval.

DAD. So…

FAY. So.

Dad takes another sip.

I have a question.

DAD. Shoot.

FAY. Do you know why Mom brought us to the bridge?

A small moment.

DAD. What?

FAY. Why Mom brought us to the bridge? Why she made us walk across it…

DAD. It's a tourist thing.
It's a thing tourists do.
FAY. I know.
Which is why I was wondering…
DAD. I don't know. Your mother always had her reasons for things.
FAY. I wanted to know if you knew her reason—
DAD. No.
No I don't.

>Dad struggles to find the right words.

And, Fay, I don't appreciate you blaming your—
FAY. I'm not blaming her.
DAD. You've just asked about the bridge / and your mother a lot these days.
FAY. Well, that is for obvious reasons.
DAD. I don't appreciate it.
FAY. All right then.

>They sip on the whiskey.
>They let it go down.

DAD. Your mother, she…she was the loud-silent type. She could make a lot of noise, a lot of demands, a lot of orders, a lot of laughter…and then you'd find her sitting quietly, staring at the moon or at the water. I loved that about her…her ability to go between the two…her ability to connect and disconnect…

She always liked the bridge. Even when we were dating, she liked to park and stare at it. I never understood it, but you do a lot of things you don't understand when you fall in love with a person. I did a lot of staring over bridges and at moons when I fell in love with your mother.

We moved here because of the view of it from your room.
Oh but the bridge will look so beautiful, she said when we walked up here.
It was too expensive, I told her. Much too much, but she needed it.
The view, the view.
The fucking view.

Look at this fucking view.

I don't know why she was obsessed with this bridge, Fay.

FAY. Okay.

DAD. I just know she liked it.
She liked the water.
That's all I can tell you.

FAY. Okay.

DAD. If she knew—

FAY. How would she?

> *Dad downs the rest of his whiskey and then pours more into his glass.*
> *Fay doesn't say anything about it.*
> *He motions to her, asking if she wants more.*
> *She shakes her head no.*

DAD. Someone's interested in the house so…

FAY. That's great, you said…

DAD. They'll be coming back with an offer.

FAY. Good. Good.

DAD. Yeah.
We'll have to get the rest of the stuff out of here.

FAY. Yeah.
Okay.
Some of it will be gone after tomorrow.

DAD. Yeah.

FAY. I can take some of the other boxes to my place…
There's some stuff I didn't know what to do with…

But.
I'll figure it out.

> *They sit in quiet.*
> *Dad gulps down a big swig.*
> *He looks at Fay.*

What?

> *Dad doesn't answer.*

What, Dad?

Is there something on my face?

DAD. No. I…

FAY. You're giving me a weird look—

DAD. I thought it would have been you.

FAY. Huh?

DAD. I thought you'd have been the one. To jump.

> *The lights flicker. Wildly.*
> *The sound in the world begins to distort.*
> *Fay feels like she has been hit in the face.*
> *Shot in the chest.*
> *Her breath leaves her.*
> *Her body begins its shock wave.*
> *Her temperature rises.*
> *She is already sweating and it has only been a few seconds.*
> *She tries to recalibrate.*

FAY. Excuse me?

DAD. If I had had to guess… I thought / you were the one who…

FAY. Maybe you've had too much to—

DAD. Not Judith.

Not Judy.

You…you I could see doing it. You've just always been that way. A little difficult. A little quiet. A little depressed. A little angry. We even talked about it…your mother and me. Kept our eyes on you in high school. You never were a happy child.

> *The lights flicker. Wildly.*

FAY. Dad…

DAD. I just couldn't see her… I didn't even know to worry about that with her… Judy always seemed fine. Great. Judy was the one we could count on. Judy was the one who was going to take care of us, of me. But now I just have you and… I'm not saying I wish it'd been you… I'm just saying that I thought you'd have been the one to jump

> *The sound of shoes.*
> *It sounds a bit cold and distorted.*
> *The world begins to stop.*

FAY. Dad, that's…that's…that's—

It goes dark and quiet.
The sound of the shoes becomes the sound of Fay's breath
and her heart.
The sounds are loud.
They're amplified.

And when the lights come back up, suddenly, we are back on
the bridge.
Hopkins is there and so is Fay.
And the other sounds linger.
The world is figuring itself out.

HOPKINS. Fay.

Fay.

Fay.

Come in, Fay…

FAY. They always thought it would be me, but it is Judy.

HOPKINS. Huh?

FAY. My parents.

HOPKINS. What are you talking about, Fay?

FAY. Judy is the one that jumps.

HOPKINS. …That…jumps?

FAY. Yes, Judy is the one that jumps.

Not me.

HOPKINS. …

FAY. Judy is the jumper.

HOPKINS. …

FAY. Judy is my sister.

HOPKINS. …

FAY. Have I told you that?

A sound of a splash.
Hopkins and Fay look over the side of the bridge.
Fay rubs the back of her head as if she just felt a sharp pain.
Judy enters.
She walks the length of the bridge.

Fay and Hopkins don't notice.
Judy exits.
Fay and Hopkins look at each other.

HOPKINS. Is?

FAY. What?

HOPKINS. You said she is the one that jumps.

FAY. I did?

HOPKINS. Yeah.

FAY. Oh.

HOPKINS. I don't think you should be up here now.

FAY. Hopkins...

HOPKINS. I'm serious. I don't think—

FAY. She jumps.
I don't.

HOPKINS. Fay—

FAY. She jumped. I won't.

HOPKINS. Let me take you home.

FAY. No.

> *Fay holds on to the railing.*

My sister Judy jumped forty-seven days ago.

HOPKINS. I'm sorry, Fay.

FAY. You don't have to worry.
I don't have the urge.
I am too strongly controlled by that gene you mentioned. I'm too strongly under Darwin's spell.

HOPKINS. That doesn't... You could still feel—

FAY. Why didn't you jump, Hopkins?

HOPKINS. We already talked about this.

> *The sound of a splash.*
> *Fay rubs the back of her head as if she just felt a sharp pain.*
> *Judy enters as they talk.*
> *She walks across the bridge, as she did before.*
> *They don't notice.*

Judy exits.
Fay gets more agitated during the following.

FAY. I want to know.

HOPKINS. What?

FAY. What stopped you?

HOPKINS. It isn't like something I can explain.

FAY. Explain it goddammit!
Explain it.

HOPKINS. Me.

FAY. What?

HOPKINS. I stopped myself.

FAY. Yeah but what does that mean?

HOPKINS. I don't know, Fay.
You.
The fact that you started singing along with me.
The way the light hits your face.
Or maybe it was the car that drove by with the baby sitting in the back.
Or the wind.
Or the stars.
Or the fact that I had to pee and who wants to die while they have to pee.
Or maybe it was the chance of survival and pain.
Or maybe it was the lack of the chance of survival and pain.
I don't know.

> *Fay huffs.*

I'm not your sister, Fay.

> *Fay quietly cries.*
> *She whispers.*

FAY. I know.

HOPKINS. Why have you been on this bridge, Fay?

FAY. ...

...

...

HOPKINS. Why have you been walking the bridge?

The sound of a splash followed by a flicker and the sound of shoes.
Fay looks up and around and brings her hands to her head as if it throbs.
Judy enters.
She walks around Hopkins.
She is in front of him.
He doesn't notice.
Fay sees her this time.
Hopkins fades away.
Somehow.
We don't notice him anymore.
Even if he is still there.
A trick of light, perhaps.

JUDY. Oh hi.

FAY. Hi.

JUDY. What are you doing up here?

FAY. Vaping.

> *A vape falls from above.*
> *She catches it.*

JUDY. This is a weird place to vape.

FAY. This is a weird place to walk.

JUDY. It's outside.
It's a beautiful view.

FAY. Both of those reasons work for the vaping thing.

> *There's a gust of wind.*

JUDY. It's windy up here.

FAY. How are you, Judy?

> *There's a small light shift.*

JUDY. Oh I'm fine

> *A small moment.*

FAY. How are you, Judy?

JUDY. Okay

> *These next ones ramp up in speed and volume.*

FAY. How are you, Judy?

JUDY. Oh you know

FAY. How are you, Judy?

JUDY. Meh

FAY. How are you, Judy?

JUDY. Who knows?

FAY. How are you, Judy?

JUDY. Tired

FAY. How are you, Judy?

JUDY. Lonely

FAY. How are you, Judy?

JUDY. I lost my job

FAY. How are you, Judy?

JUDY. Russell doesn't love me anymore.

FAY. How are you, Judy?

JUDY. Worried about the future.

FAY. How are you, Judy?

JUDY. I tried to pray for the first time in years.

FAY. How are you, Judy?

JUDY. Barely getting by.

FAY. How are you, Judy?

JUDY. I couldn't see the reason to get out of bed this morning.

FAY. How are you, Judy?

JUDY. I don't see this getting any better.

FAY. How are you, Judy?

JUDY. Fine.

FAY. How are you, Judy?

JUDY. Fine.

FAY. HOW ARE YOU, JUDY?

JUDY. FINE FINE FINE FINE FINE We all say we are fine and that we don't need anything and what we really want to say is fucking help me GOD because I am so far from fine and You are not doing shit about it. And we get angry I get angry because if You are real, God, if You are so damn real, then why aren't You doing shit to help me feel better? And if You aren't real then why the hell am I praying to You.

FAY. How are you, Judy?

JUDY. I'm fine. I don't need anything. Honestly.

FAY. Honestly?

JUDY. Honestly I don't need anything. Honestly.
You are beautiful. Honestly.
That didn't hurt my feelings. I understand. Honestly.
I think it would be a great day to leave the house and my comfort zone and do a list of things I don't really feel like doing. Honestly. Honestly. Honestly. Honestly.
Honestly I've wanted to jump off this bridge since I was twelve and Mom brought us here for the first time and I could see the water and the rocks and I wondered how much it would hurt to touch down on them and feel the bones breaking. I didn't want to die I just wanted to feel the impact. Honestly. There's a phrase for that, / l'appel du vide.

FAY. L'appel du vide.

> *Judy looks at her.*

You wrote the phrase in your planner. I went through your planner. You don't have a journal…diary…blog…so I went through your planner.

JUDY. You wanted a reason?

FAY. Yes.

JUDY. As I got older…there was one thing after another and…I'd walk the bridge and stare at the water and one day I realized just looking wasn't going to save me.
My reason is my reason. You probably wouldn't think of it as a good reason. But it is. Because it is mine.
Honestly.
But I'm fine.

Remember when Mom would walk us across the bridge?

> *Fay nods.*

We'd complain because we always had to walk back to get to the car,

but she made us do it anyway. And she'd always stop and point out her favorite part of the city. Those were good days.
Even though we hated them.

> *There is time here. Some time for each of them to calm down in their own ways. To come back to whatever reality this is.*

FAY. Judy?

JUDY. Yes?

FAY. I found cigarettes. In your car. I had to go through your car.

JUDY. I secretly smoke.

FAY. You do?

JUDY. Sometimes I bum cigarettes off of guys at bars.

FAY. A lot of people do that.

JUDY. Yeah but did you expect me to?

FAY. No.
No I didn't.

JUDY. See?

FAY. And the fact that you wear hot-pink underwear.
I had to go through your clothes…

JUDY. I like to keep it exciting underneath, you know?

FAY. I didn't know. Tell me other things. Other things I don't know.

JUDY. There's nothing to tell.

FAY. That can't be—

JUDY. I only like vanilla ice cream.
And I lied about how my hair got cut in the fourth grade.
I cut it.
In the bathroom.

FAY. Pretty sure everyone knew that.

JUDY. Oh.

FAY. More please.

JUDY. I always wanted a garden. I planted a tree in my backyard but it never grew.
Russell hit me for the first time on our third date.
I think I should have been born English because I really like grass

and sheep.
I saw a sheep once that was, like, shedding—is that what you call it?
And it looked like it had a sweater half on and I was like huh that
makes sense because that's how we get our sweaters.
I think I make no sense.

FAY. That makes two of us.

Judy?

JUDY. What?

FAY. You never told me about Russell.

> *Judy shrugs.*

JUDY. Ask me something else.

FAY. What went through your mind?

JUDY. When?

FAY. When…when.
When you…

> *Judy shrugs.*

JUDY. I jump.
I leap.
I hit the water.

FAY. Did you regret it? Did you have second—

JUDY. Stop.

FAY. Why? Why here? Why this way?

JUDY. I hear the water just sweeps you under.

FAY. Really?

JUDY. No.
You read that, Fay.
Those aren't my words.

FAY. I want *your* words.

JUDY. Pull out your phone.

> *Fay pulls out her phone.*

There's a voicemail you haven't listened to.
From me. From like six months ago.
You come to the bridge and you look at your phone because you

want to play the message and then you don't.

FAY. I don't mean those kind of words.

JUDY. That's all you get.

> *Fay puts her phone away.*

FAY. For god's sake, tell me something else, Judy.
Tell me something!

JUDY. Stop, Fay.

> *Judy touches Fay's arm.*
> *Fay flinches.*

FAY. I feel... I feel like I should apologize or something...

JUDY. For what?

FAY. For not—

JUDY. Please.

> *A moment.*

FAY. The urn is blue.
Not like navy blue.
Or sky blue.
Or even midnight blue.
Well, really it was a greenish blue, somewhere between teal and blue.
It reminded me of the ocean.
Or deep water.
I've never seen an urn that color.

I mean I guess I never saw an urn before.

I keep seeing that blue everywhere. All around me. I suppose it has always been there and I just never really noticed before but...

> *Judy motions for the vape.*
> *Fay hands it to her.*
> *It takes her a moment, but she figures out how it works.*
> *She enjoys it.*

JUDY. Apple?

FAY. Yeah.

JUDY. I like blue.

FAY. We know. That's why we chose it.

JUDY. Yeah.

FAY. Yeah.

JUDY. You know, I'm not here, Fay.
I'm not here.
I'm not your dead ghost sister coming to talk to you and make amends.

> *Judy exits with the vape.*
> *The world stops again.*
> *The sound of shoes.*
> *This is the first time it seems like the shoes are walking away.*
> *It goes dark and quiet.*
> *We then hear Fay's breath.*
> *It's loud.*
> *It's amplified.*
> *It's being blasted in surround sound.*
> *And when the lights come back up, suddenly, we are back in the house but maybe we are also on the bridge.*
> *Dad is back there too.*
> *Hopkins is still there.*
> *And the lights flicker, but less intensely than before.*

DAD. I just thought you were the one who I needed to worry about.

FAY. I don't know what that means.

DAD. You were—

FAY. I could say the same about you, Dad. I mean who really thought you'd outlive Mom?
Mom and Judy for that matter? Who really thought that?

I sure as hell didn't.

Is this what you've been thinking these last few weeks? Did you think it when we were at the police station? When filing the missing person's report? Or did you think it at the funeral home? Or when I had to identify her? Or maybe it was at the service, at her house, in the car, when you were finishing your second bottle of—

DAD. Fay, I didn't—

FAY. I'm sorry Judy isn't here to take care of you, Dad. I'm sorry you're stuck with me. I'm sorry I'm stuck with you.

Fay throws her glass.
It breaks.
They don't say anything.
After a moment, Fay storms out and Dad exits.
And then Fay walks back on and Hopkins is still there.
And they are on the bridge.
Lights flicker but less intensely.

HOPKINS. Parents can be shit.

FAY. Huh?

HOPKINS. Your dad saying that is shitty.

FAY. Oh.
Yeah.

HOPKINS. Your sister…she's the one…?

FAY. In the news, yeah.
They, uh, found her two days later…

HOPKINS. After reading that, I wondered… I wondered if I had seen her. Up here. Sometime.

Fay looks at him closely.

But I didn't recognize her picture. Not the one in the article.

FAY. Oh.

HOPKINS. Yeah.

Brief moment.

FAY. When they found her…she was like shredded—

HOPKINS. Fay…

Fay looks at him.

FAY. Suffice it to say according to your theory she wanted it real bad.

HOPKINS. I was spouting bullshit.

FAY. I know.

HOPKINS. I don't know what I'm talking about.

We have no idea what she—

FAY. That's just it.
We had no idea.
Not one.

Does someone know, Hopkins? Does someone know about you? Would someone have said "Oh fuck we knew he was feeling shitty we should have done something"? Or would they have been interviewed and had to say over and over again "We had no idea"? No fucking idea.

> *Hopkins shrugs.*

HOPKINS. I don't know.
You know.
Now.

FAY. They aren't going to come looking for me if your body washes up. Assuming it even does.
Assuming someone even notices you.
Assuming...

HOPKINS. Let's get outta here, Fay.

> *Fay pulls out her phone.*

FAY. She left me a voicemail like six months ago. I never checked it. Never deleted it.

HOPKINS. Do you...want...to check it...now?

> *The lights flicker but less intensely.*
> *She goes to the voicemail.*
> *She plays it.*

JUDY'S VOICE. Hey pipsqueak it's me. Dad's birthday is next week and we should probably...we should probably do something right? Like a cake? Do you want to get Dad's cake or me? You live closer to that fancy bakery so you should...but...I can...if you want... Just... just call me back. Like really call me back. Don't not call me back.

> *The voicemail ends.*
> *Fay brings the phone to her chest.*
> *If there is ever a moment that Fay breaks down, it is here. It is now.*
> *Hopkins doesn't know what to do. He tries to comfort, but doesn't know what would be comforting.*
> *It isn't a loud breakdown, but when she calms down, it feels quieter.*

FAY. She got the cake. I didn't.

HOPKINS. That's okay.

FAY. I forgot it was his birthday. She reminded me to get a card.

HOPKINS. When's his birthday?

FAY. April 28th.

HOPKINS. Give me your phone.

> *Fay hands him the phone.*

FAY. What are you doing?

HOPKINS. Putting his birthday in your calendar. And making it repeat every year.
I do the same for my mom's.

FAY. Oh.

> *He pushes a few buttons and then hands the phone back to her.*
> *Fay sort of smiles and then takes a deep breath.*

Okay.

HOPKINS. What?

FAY. Let's get out of here.

HOPKINS. Okay.

FAY. But I'm driving.

HOPKINS. You sure that's a good idea?

FAY. No.
But I'm driving.

HOPKINS. …Okay…

FAY. You didn't bike here, did you?

HOPKINS. No.
No.
I drove.
Biking gets tedious…

FAY. Yeah.
Okay
Lead the way.

HOPKINS. Oh I thought you wanted—

FAY. I said I wanted to drive.
I didn't say I had a car.
I walked here.

HOPKINS. Oh, um…it's this way.

FAY. You first.

> *Hopkins starts to walk.*
> *Every once in a while he turns to look back at Fay.*
> *Fay walks, but she doesn't look ahead.*
> *She looks out over the edge of the bridge.*
> *They exit.*

11.

> *Next day. 1 A.M.*

> *It is night.*
> *Late night.*
> *And we are back in the living room of the house.*
> *In a chair, Dad sleeps with one little light on.*
> *He has a full glass of whiskey, way more than he should,*
> *next to him.*
> *He is holding Judy's violin.*
> *Fay enters.*
> *She stands and watches him for a few moments.*
> *He shifts.*
> *She breathes.*
> *His eyes open slowly.*
> *The two of them let the quiet sink in around them before*
> *they speak.*

FAY. You stayed.

DAD. Yeah.

FAY. How'd you know I'd come back?

DAD. I didn't.

> *Fay nods.*

You know, you're my only…

FAY. I know.

DAD. I'm…sorry. I don't know what came over me.

FAY. It's okay.

DAD. It's not.

FAY. Yeah, but it was the truth. Is. Even for me. I know what you meant... Judy wasn't... I'm the type. She isn't.

> *Dad nods, but doesn't say anything.*
> *He picks up his glass and offers it to Fay.*
> *She silently turns it down.*

DAD. Where'd you go?

FAY. The bridge.

> *Dad gets visibly upset.*

DAD. What?!

FAY. I go there sometimes.

DAD. Why?

FAY. Because the water, the view is soothing. Was.
Because we went when we were little.
Because I can feel her...them...there.

DAD. Don't you dare jump, Fay. Do you hear me? Don't you dare leave me.

> *A long moment.*

FAY. We're stuck with each other. You know? In a good way. We're a team.

> *They let themselves feel that.*
> *But there is no comforting of the other.*
> *They are on their own comfort-wise.*

It's late.
Are you going to be okay?

DAD. Your old bed is still up there. I can sleep there.

FAY. Okay.

DAD. Fay.

FAY. Yeah.

DAD. Do you need any money?

FAY. No.

DAD. Do you need a ride home?

FAY. No.

DAD. Do you need—

FAY. I don't need anything.

DAD. Okay.

> *A moment.*
> *Fay turns to leave.*

I thought we should keep her violin.

FAY. Okay.

DAD. She really hated playing it.

> *Dad laughs a small laugh.*

FAY. We all did. She was so bad.

DAD. Yeah. But we'd have to sit through her in-home recitals.

FAY. And Mom would always make some kind of treat. Like cupcakes. And she'd whisper that she made them for us.

DAD. As payment to keep our mouths shut.

FAY. Yeah.

> *They chuckle.*

DAD. Can you bring me sometime?

FAY. Where?

DAD. The bridge?
I'd like to go…sometime.

FAY. …

…

…

Okay.
We can do that.

DAD. Good…good… Get home safe, Fay.

FAY. Sure thing, Dad.

> *Fay exits.*
> *Dad takes another sip of whiskey.*
> *Blackout.*

12.

A week later.

A bright afternoon.
Hopkins stands on the bridge.
He looks like he is waiting.
Then he smiles and gives a half wave.
Fay and Dad enter.
Dad seems unsure about walking on the bridge.
Fay attempts to be patient with him.
Fay carries a small bag.
Flowers may peek out from the bag.
They meet together center.

HOPKINS. Hey.

FAY. Hey.
Uh.
Dad, this is Hopkins.
Hopkins, this is my dad.

DAD. You're the guy she meets on the bridge.

HOPKINS. Happy to know I've been brought up.

DAD. What kind of name is Hopkins?

       Hopkins shrugs.

HOPKINS. A family one.
I guess.

DAD. You related to the people who run Johns Hopkins?

HOPKINS. I don't / know...   FAY. Dad.

DAD. I'm just wondering.

       A moment.

What's your last name?

FAY. Come on, Dad.   HOPKINS. Um, Scott.

DAD. Huh.

FAY. It is like your parents switched the order.

HOPKINS. Yeah.

Maybe that's why they did.

You know.

Since my last name is a first name.

FAY and DAD. Yeah.

> *A moment.*
> *Dad turns his attention outward.*

DAD. So this is where...

FAY. Yeah.

If you squint you can see the house.

> *He squints.*
> *Hopkins squints but has no idea what the house looks like.*
> *Fay just watches them.*

DAD. Oh.

Yeah.

FAY. Do you think she...

> *Fay fades off. The three of them take in the bridge and the sight and the noises.*
> *A long moment.*

DAD. I think I'll leave now.

FAY. You only just got here. We were going to do—

DAD. I...I was never a fan of bridges. I am not like your mother... or you girls.

FAY. I know.

DAD. I don't like heights.

FAY. Yeah.

DAD. And...and...well...I...I have unpacking to do.

FAY. Okay.

DAD. Yes.

FAY. I'll see you Sunday.

DAD. Okay.

> *Dad turns to leave.*
> *He then turns back and he gives Fay a big hug.*

Hopkins looks away. He gives them a moment.
Dad kisses Fay on the top of her head.
He whispers something in her ear.
We imagine he says he is sorry.
We imagine he says thank you.
We imagine he says he loves her.
We imagine he says they'll be okay.
Though we won't ever know for sure.
Fay smiles and nods.
Dad gives a half wave over the bridge with one hand.
And then he walks away.

FAY. I wanted to do this whole thing.
I wanted to drop lilies from up here.
I wanted to watch them hit the water.

HOPKINS. We can.
I'll do it with you.

> *Fay nods.*
> *She opens her bag and brings out the lilies.*
> *She looks at Hopkins.*

FAY. What kind of flower would you want?

HOPKINS. What?

FAY. If you were to do it.
What kind of flower would you want me to let go for you?
Morbid…I know…but—

HOPKINS. I've always liked Gerbera daisies.

FAY. Okay.

> *Fay is surprised by the specificity. A moment.*

HOPKINS. This would be the time for me to say that you'll never have to do that for me.

FAY. Would it be the truth?

> *Hopkins shrugs.*

HOPKINS. I hope so.

> *A quiet settles in again.*

You won't have to.

FAY. …

HOPKINS. Positive thinking, right…
What about you?

FAY. Huh?

HOPKINS. Which flower would you want me to let go of for you?

> *Fay thinks.*

FAY. Daffodils.

HOPKINS. All right.

FAY. But really anything but a carnation.

HOPKINS. Okay.

> *They turn and look out.*
> *No words are spoken.*
> *Fay may be saying something in her head.*
> *Then she holds a lily out over the railing.*
> *She takes a deep breath.*
> *She goes to drop it.*
> *The lights bump out.*
> *And then, quickly, the lights bump back on.*
> *And the bridge is empty.*
>
> *And then Judy enters.*
> *She is in the Converse.*
>
> *She is in jeans and a button-down top and she looks like she could be just taking a pit stop.*
>
> *Like she just wanted to go for a walk.*
>
> *We may not see these people but the world goes on around her. A runner runs behind her. Someone goes by on a bike. A couple walks by.*
>
> *No one takes her in.*
>
> *No one gives her a second glance.*
>
> *She doesn't exactly stand still, but she isn't exactly walking at a normal speed.*

She isn't crying.

She doesn't even look sad.

She looks up.

She looks right and she looks left.

She then looks forward.

A lily falls from above.

She catches it and smiles.

End of Play

PROPERTY LIST
(Use this space to create props lists for your production)

SOUND EFFECTS

(Use this space to create sound effects lists for your production)

Dear reader,

Thank you for supporting playwrights by purchasing this acting edition! You may not know that Dramatists Play Service was founded, in 1936, by the Dramatists Guild and a number of prominent play agents to protect the rights and interests of play-wrights. To this day, we are still a small company committed to our partnership with the Guild, and by proxy all playwrights, established and aspiring, working in the English language.

Because of our status as a small, independent publisher, we respect-fully reiterate that this text may not be distributed or copied in any way, or uploaded to any file-sharing sites, including ones you might think are private. Photocopying or electronically distributing books means both DPS and the playwright are not paid for the work, and that ultimately hurts playwrights everywhere, as our profits are shared with the Guild.

We also hope you want to perform this play! Plays are wonderful to read, but even better when seen. If you are interested in performing or producing the play, please be aware that performance rights must be obtained through Dramatists Play Service. This is true for *any* public performance, even if no one is getting paid or admission is not being charged. Again, playwrights often make their sole living from performance royalties, so performing plays without paying the royalty is ultimately a loss for a real writer.

This acting edition is the **only approved text for performance**. There may be other editions of the play available for sale from other publishers, but DPS has worked closely with the playwright to ensure this published text reflects their desired text of all future productions. If you have purchased a revised edition (sometimes referred to as other types of editions, like "Broadway Edition," or "[Year] Edition"), that is the only edition you may use for perfor-mance, unless explicitly stated in writing by Dramatists Play Service.

Finally, this script cannot be changed without written permission from Dramatists Play Service. If a production intends to change the script in any way—including casting against the writer's intentions for characters, removing or changing "bad" words, or making other cuts however small—without permission, they are breaking the law. And, perhaps more importantly, changing an artist's work. Please don't do that!

We are thrilled that this play has made it into your hands. We hope you love it as much as we do, and thank you for helping us keep the American theater alive and vital.

Note on Songs/Recordings, Images, or Other Production Design Elements

Be advised that Dramatists Play Service, Inc., neither holds the rights to nor grants permission to use any songs, recordings, images, or other design elements mentioned in the play. It is the responsibility of the producing theater/organization to obtain permission of the copyright owner(s) for any such use. Additional royalty fees may apply for the right to use copyrighted materials.

For any songs/recordings, images, or other design elements mentioned in the play, works in the public domain may be substituted. It is the producing theater/organization's responsibility to ensure the substituted work is indeed in the public domain. Dramatists Play Service, Inc., cannot advise as to whether or not a song/arrangement/recording, image, or other design element is in the public domain.